MW00535129

This book
belongs to

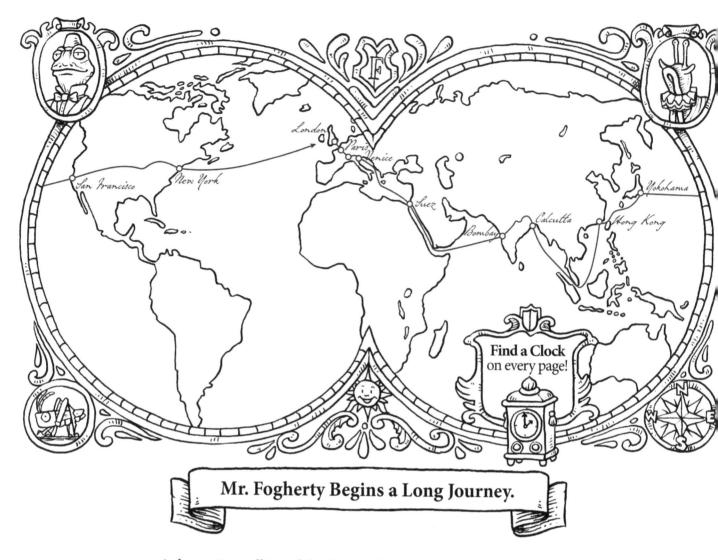

Mr. Fogherty Begins a Long Journey.

A dramatic retelling of the classic adventure, starring Mr. Fogherty,
the independently wealthy eccentric, and Snail, the former circus performer turned valet.

Will they succeed in returning to London within 80 days, or is the long journey too much
for a small green frog and his shell-bound companion?

Bring your color vision to life and embark on a journey filled with whimsy and wonder.
For coloring enthusiasts and frog lovers of all ages!

See more at rjhampson.com

 **russelljamesart**

Published by Hop Skip Jump. PO Box 1324 Buderim Queensland Australia 4556
First published 2024. Copyright © 2024 R.J. Hampson.

ISBN: 978-1-922472-32-8

Please Note: Place names and modes of transport shown in this book are typical of 1892 or completely invented by the author. Please do not attempt this journey without more current information and adult supervision.

Using this book

Find a quiet place away from distractions. Relax and immerse yourself in the process of coloring as you explore the details of each fantastic illustration.

This book is best suited to color pencils or markers. Wet mediums should be used sparingly. Slide a card or sheets of paper behind the illustration you are coloring to avoid marker bleed through.

Find fresh coloring pages by signing up to Russell's newsletter. Get free downloadable pages and updates on new books at -

rjhampson.com/coloring

Daily Schedule:

8:00am	- Rise
8:23am	- Tea & Toast
9:37am	- Shaving Water (86°F)
9:40am	- Bathe
11:30am	- To the Reform Club
12:00am	- Return Home to Bed

MR FOGHERTY'S CLOCK

Every Day - Location: England

Where Mr. Fogherty's life runs like clockwork.

THE REFORM CLUB

Day 1 - Location: England

Where Mr. Fogherty plays games of whist with friends ~ Discussions of global travel ~ A wager is made.

THE BARE ESSENTIALS

Day 1 - Location: England

Where Mr. Fogherty and Snail must prepare for their adventure.

CHARING CROSS STATION

Day 1 - Location: England

Where Mr. Fogherty and Snail depart for the Continent.

PARIS
Day 2 - Location: France
Where Mr. Fogherty enjoys a quiet repast at a local cafe ~ The menu is disquieting.

THE ORIENT EXPRESS

Day 3 - Location: On Board

Where Mr. Fogherty and Snail travel in comfort.

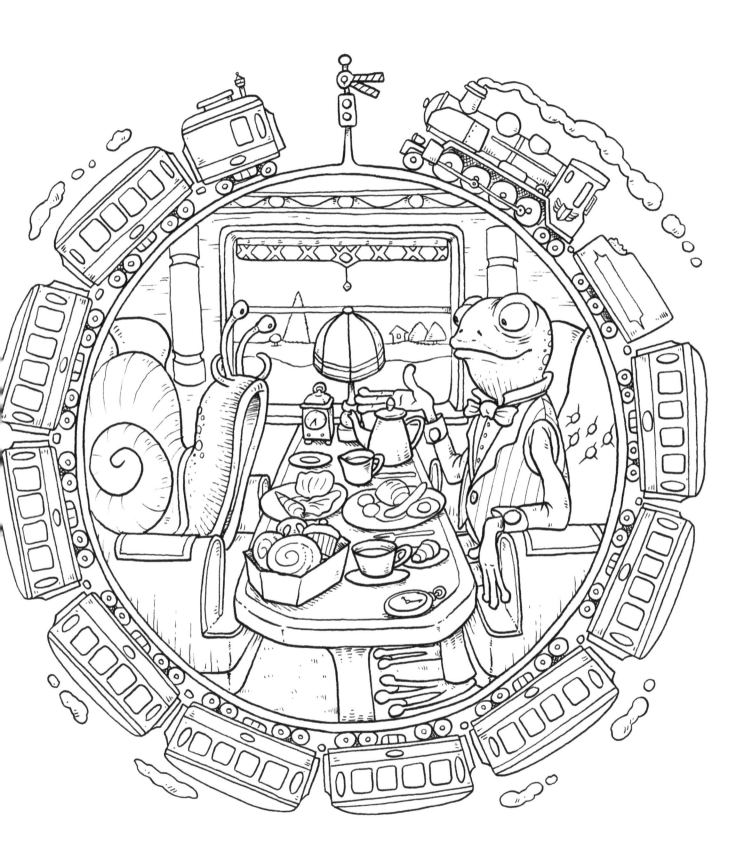

THE ALPINE WAY

Day 3 - Location: Switzerland

Where Mr. Fogherty takes a brisk hike over the Alps.

VENICE

Day 4 - Location: Italy

Where Mr. Fogherty is inspired to sketch the architecture ~ Snail takes a trip in the canals ~
The local delicacy 'gelato' is consumed and enjoyed.

PROMENADE

Day 5 - Location: The Mediterranean Sea

Where Mr. Fogherty meets a fellow passenger en route to the Suez Canal on board the Mongolia.

THE CUSTOMS OFFICE

Day 7 - Location: Egypt

Where Mr. Fogherty must have his passport stamped close to lunch time ~ A Customs Officer looks peckish.

PHARAOH'S FISHING FOLLIES

Day 8 - Location: Egypt

Where Mr. Fogherty dreams of the days of the fishing Pharaohs.

SETTING SAIL

Day 10 - Location: The Arabian Sea

Where Mr. Fogherty and Snail sail across the Arabian Sea in a Dhow.

A SPOT OF SIGHTSEEING

Day 16 - Location: India

Where Mr. Fogherty and Snail experience the famous sights of the Taj Mahal.

CORACLE CASTAWAYS

Day 18 - Location: India

Where the travelers temporarily travel at a more languid pace.

PANGOLIN PALANQUIN

Day 21 - Location: India

Where Mr. Fogherty and Snail discover an unexpected end to the railroad ~
Alternative arrangements are made en route to Calcutta.

TEA FOR TWO

Day 34 - Location: Hong Kong

Where Mr. Fogherty is pleasantly distracted whilst awaiting a Steamer to Japan.

LATE

Day 35 - Location: Hong Kong

Where Mr. Fogherty misses his connection to Japan ~ Snail is alone on board without resources.

TOGETHER AGAIN

Day 38 - Location: Japan

Where Snail has found temporary employment ~ The adventurers are reunited at a traveling circus.

JAPAN

Day 40 - Location: Japan

Where Mr. Fogherty enjoys meeting the locals and hearing their tales.

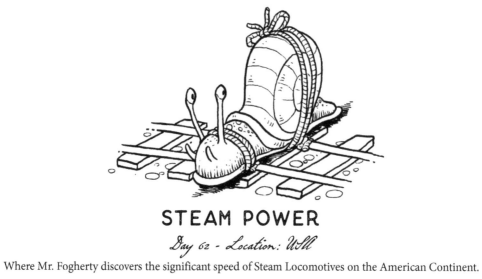

STEAM POWER

Day 62 - Location: USA

Where Mr. Fogherty discovers the significant speed of Steam Locomotives on the American Continent.

OVER THE PLAINS

Day 66 - Location: USA

Where a lack of track forces Mr. Fogherty to continue his journey by Wind Powered Sledge.

THE ART OF FLIGHT

Day 69 - Location: USA

Where Mr. Fogherty journeys high above by Balloon.

CAPTAIN'S CHALLENGE

Day 78 - Location: The Atlantic Ocean

Where Mr. Fogherty uses his skills to command a Steamer to Liverpool.

HUZZAH!

Day 79 - Location: England

Where Mr. Fogherty's successful journey is celebrated.

HOME AT LAST

Day 80 - Location: England

Where Mr. Fogherty's daily routine is restored ~ The comforts of home are enjoyed.

Discover so much more to color!

Find new coloring pages by signing up to R.J. Hampson's newsletter.
Get free downloadable pages, monthly coloring sheets,
and updates on new books at -

rjhampson.com/coloring

Thanks for choosing this coloring book.
If you enjoyed it, please consider leaving a review.
It will help to let more people in on the experience
plus you'd certainly make this illustrator very happy!

More books in this series

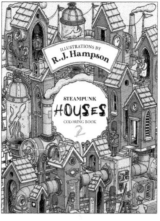

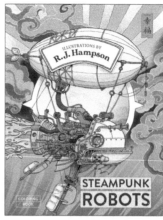

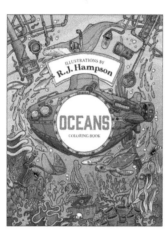

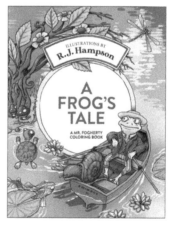

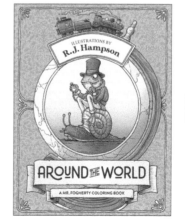

COLLECT THEM ALL!

See flip-throughs for all coloring books at **rjhampson.com**

Printed in the USA
CPSIA information can be obtained
at www.ICGtesting.com
LVHW062042190424
777809LV00005B/103